BLACK OUT LOUD

BLACK

DRAWINGS BY

ALVIN HOLLINGSWORTH

OUT LOUD

An Anthology of Modern Poems

by Black Americans

EDITED BY **ARNOLD ADOFF**

THE MACMILLAN COMPANY

FOR MY DAUGHTER LEIGH

AND FOR ALL PROUD POETS

ACKNOWLEDGMENTS   Thanks are due to the following
for permission to include copyrighted selections:

Imamu Ameer Baraka (LeRoi Jones) for "Black Art" (dedication
page). Reprinted by permission of Ronald Hobbs Literary Agency.

Black Dialogue Publications for "For Some Poets," "i remember
. . . ," "The Blues Today" and "i used to wrap my white doll up
in" from *Can I Poet with You?* by Mae Jackson, © 1969 by Mae
Jackson.

Paul Bremen Ltd. for "In defense of black poets" and "Watts"
from *The Still Voice of Harlem* by Conrad Kent Rivers, London,
1968.

Additional acknowledgments on pages 85 & 86 constitute an extension of this copyright page.

PREFACE

Langston Hughes began in the 1920's to write poetry that
changed how Black people would see themselves and their
country. Gwendolyn Brooks, Imamu Ameer Baraka (LeRoi
Jones) and hundreds of others have carried on that tradition
of honesty and art. Today, there are countless young poets
writing in classrooms, workshops and on kitchen tables. Some
of the poetry of these young writers as well as of the famous
ones is included in this collection. They write of love, hatred,
protest and pride. They write of the joy and anger of life in
our country.

This collection was compiled to introduce the works of
Black poets to the young brothers and sisters of all races. It
has been over twenty years since Arna Bontemps' anthology
of "American Negro" poetry, *Golden Slippers,* was published
for young people. *Black Out Loud* can only be a beginning
after so long a time. For every poet in this book, there are
many whose fine verse could not be included within the
space limitations of a single volume.

There are many revolutions taking place in our country
today. Some carry with them noise and smoke and blood. They
explode in headlines and newscasts. Poets make revolutions
with their words and craft. An exciting poem can have the
power of a fist. It can help bring about changes that are strong
and meaningful.

The poets in this anthology are among the change-makers.
They have seen themselves. They have seen their people and
their country. And they have created fine poems to say and
sing and shout what they feel and know and want.

Arnold Adoff

New York City
1970

"...We want
a black poem.
And a Black
world. Let the
world be a
Black Poem...."

Imamu Ameer Baraka
(LeRoi Jones)

CONTENTS

Black All Day

I Am a Poet

Perhaps You Will Remember

right on: white america

But Here I Am

You Are Loved, Awake or Dreaming

BLACK
ALL
DAY

AWARENESS

BLACK	PEOPLE	THINK
PEOPLE	BLACK	PEOPLE
THINK	PEOPLE	THINK
BLACK	PEOPLE	THINK —
THINK	BLACK.	

Don L. Lee

Black Is Best

Black is best.
        My mother forgot to tell me.
But I told her
      that black is best.
    And she says: Boy hush your mouth
I again say:
      Black is best mamma.
     And she hit me.
   But I keep saying:
      Black is best.

Larry Thompson

2

Color

Wear it
Like a banner
For the proud —
Not like a shroud.
Wear it
Like a song
Soaring high —
Not moan or cry.

Langston Hughes

Black All Day

This morning, when he looked at me,
I saw how black I was
though there was nothing I could see
to give him any cause.

But I was black all day, and mean;
and leaving none to doubt,
I showed all day what I had seen
this morning stepping out.

He looked me into rage and shame;
no less, the day was grim.
Tomorrow, by another name,
I'll do as much for him.

Raymond Richard Patterson

Blackberry Sweet

Black girl black girl
lips as curved as cherries
full as grape bunches
sweet as blackberries

Black girl black girl
when you walk you are
magic as a rising bird
or a falling star

Black girl black girl
what's your spell to make
the heart in my breast
jump   stop   shake

Dudley Randall

The Alarm Clock

Alarm clock
sure sound
loud
this mornin' . . .
remind me of the time
I sat down
in a drug store
with my
mind
away far off . . .
until the girl
and she was small
it seems to me
with yellow hair
a hangin'
smiled up and said
"I'm sorry but
we don't serve
you people
here"
and I woke up
quick
like I did this mornin'
when the
alarm
went off . . .
It don't do
to wake up
quick . . .

Mari Evans

We Own the Night

We are unfair
And unfair
We are black magicians
Black arts we make
in black labs of the heart

The fair are fair
And deathly white

The day will not save them
And we own the night

Imamu Ameer Baraka (LeRoi Jones)

Image

I cannot be hurt anymore.
I see that their arrows
are really boomerangs.

Henry Dumas

Idle Chatter

daddy drinks
lots of
beer
mama works
in people's
houses
our buildin'
stinks
like school
and girls
but some are
pretty
like my sister
and mama
was
in school
they call me
charcoal
and i ain't
black
but i don't
even
care
'cause
i'm gonna be
rich
some
day

Charles Cooper

Word Poem
(Perhaps Worth Considering)

as things be/come
let's destroy
then we can destroy
what we be/come
let's build
what we become
when we dream

Nikki Giovanni

Poem (No Name No. 2)

Bitter Black Bitterness
Black Bitter Bitterness
Bitterness Black Brothers
Bitter Black Get
Blacker Get Bitter
Get Black Bitterness
NOW

Nikki Giovanni

Washiri (Poet)

Tall
Poetic
Loud
    Black
    Angry
    Proud

Kattie M. Cumbo

A BLACK POETRY DAY

        i am waiting for
      a day when thousands
    will gather before
  shops and stores.

        i am waiting for
      a day when thousands
    of BLACKS will listen
  to the words of BLACK POETS.

        i am waiting for
      a BLACK POETRY DAY.

                        Alicia Loy Johnson

THE TRUTH

IF YOU SHOULD SEE A   M A N
walking down a crowded
street
      talking
           ALOUD
TO HIMSELF
          DON'T RUN
                IN THE
OPPOSITE DIRECTION
              BUT RUN
TOWARD HIM
        for he is a
            POET
You have NOTHING to
            Fear
FROM THE
        POET
          BUT THE

      TRUTH

Ted Joans

The Truth Is Quite Messy

Neatness, madam, has
nothing to do
with the Truth.
The Truth
is quite messy
like
a wind blown room.

William J. Harris

An Historic Moment

The man said,
after inventing poetry,
"WOW!"
and did a full somersault.

William J. Harris

For Some Poets

can — i — poet
with you roi
            can i
poet
    for
        a
          little
              while
write a poem about
The Spirit House
                can i
poet for a while?

let me
        poet
with 'cha larry
                let me
poet
    for
        a
          while
write a poem about your blackness
                                can i
poet
for
a
while.

can i
    poet
with you nikki
can i
    poet for a little taste
write a poem about your poetry
can i
just for
a day
poet
with you Marvin X
poet with you please?

Mae Jackson

The Birth of the Poet

After the good fairy
blesses him with speech,
the evil fairy snatches
him and lets him
                    fall.
                All
                        his
                                f
                                        a
                                    l
                                        l
                                            i
                                                n
                                                    g
                                                        life
                                                            he
                                                                tries
                                                                    to
                                                                        tell.

Quandra Prettyman

The Distant Drum

I am not a metaphor or symbol.
This you hear is not the wind in the trees,
Nor a cat being maimed in the street.
I am being maimed in the street.
It is I who weep, laugh, feel pain or joy,
Speak this because I exist.
This is my voice.
These words are my words,
My mouth speaks them,
My hand writes —
I am a poet.
It is my fist you hear
Beating against your ear.

Calvin C. Hernton

In defense of black poets

(for Hoyt)

The critics cry unfair
    yet the poem is born.
Some black emancipated baby
    will scratch his head
wondering why you felt compelled
    to say whatever you said.

A black poet must bear in mind
    the misery.
The color-seekers fear poems
    they can't buy for a ten-dollar
bill or with a clever contract.
    Some black kid is bound to read you.

A black poet must remember the horrors.
    The good jobs can't last forever.
It shall come to pass that the fury
    of a token revolution will fade
into the bank accounts of countless blacks
    and freedom-loving whites.

The brilliant novels shall pass
    into the archives of a 'keep cool
we've done enough for you' generation:
    the movement organizations already
await their monthly checks from Downtown
    and

only the forgotten wails of a few black
    poets and artists
shall survive the then of then,
    the now of now.

Conrad Kent Rivers

My Poem

i am 25 years old
black female poet
wrote a poem asking
nigger can you kill
if they kill me
it won't stop
the revolution

i have been robbed
it looked like they knew
that i was to be hit
they took my tv
my two rings
my piece of african print
and my two guns
if they take my life
it won't stop
the revolution

my phone is tapped
my mail is opened
they've caused me to turn
on all my old friends
and all my new lovers
if i hate all black
people
and all negroes
it won't stop
the revolution

i'm afraid to tell
my roommate where i'm going
and scared to tell
people if i'm coming
if i sit here
for the rest
of my life
it won't stop
the revolution

if i never write
another poem
or short story
if i flunk out
of grad school
if my car is reclaimed
and my record player
won't play
and if i never see
a peaceful day
or do a meaningful
black thing
it won't stop
the revolution

the revolution
is in the streets
and if i stay on
the 5th floor
it will go on
if i never do
anything
it will go on

Nikki Giovanni

PERHAPS
YOU WILL
REMEMBER

Ali

Ali
Is our prince
Regal and Black
A glass that could fall
but never break
A flower without rain
that never could die
Ali
Is our prince

Djangatolum (Lloyd M. Corbin, Jr.)

Langston

standing on 127th the
smell of collards
the sound
of cueballs and the
Primitive Church
of The Universal God he
told it like it
was . . .

Mari Evans

Martin Luther King Jr.

A man went forth with gifts.

He was a prose poem.
He was a tragic grace.
He was a warm music.

He tried to heal the vivid volcanoes.
His ashes are
    reading the world.

His Dream still wishes to anoint
    the barricades of faith and of control.

His word still burns the center of the sun,
    above the thousands and the
    hundred thousands.

The word was Justice. It was spoken.

So it shall be spoken.
So it shall be done.

Gwendolyn Brooks

Assassination

it was wild
the
bullet hit high.
           (the throat-neck)
& from everywhere:
           the motel, from under bushes and cars,
           from around corners and across streets,
           out of garbage cans and from rat holes
           in the earth
they came running.
with
guns
drawn
they came running
toward the King —
           all of them
           fast and sure —
as if
the King
was going to fire back.
they came running,
fast and sure,
in the
wrong
direction.

Don L. Lee

The Funeral of Martin Luther King, Jr.

His headstone said
FREE AT LAST, FREE AT LAST
But death is a slave's freedom
We seek the freedom of free men
And the construction of a world
Where Martin Luther King could have lived and preached
    non-violence

Atlanta, April 9, 1968

Nikki Giovanni

MY ACE OF SPADES

MALCOLM X SPOKE TO ME and sounded you
Malcolm X said this to me & THEN TOLD you that!
Malcolm X whispered in my ears but SCREAMED
     on you!
Malcolm X praised me & thus condemned you
Malcolm X smiled at me & sneered at you
Malcolm X made me proud & so you got scared
Malcolm X told me to HURRY & you began to worry
Malcolm X sang to me but GROWLED AT YOU!!
Malcolm X words freed me & they frightened you
Malcolm X tol' it lak it DAMN SHO' IS!!
Malcolm X said that everybody will be FREE!!
Malcolm X told both of us the TRUTH . . . . . .
                    now didn't he?

Ted Joans

It Was a Funky Deal

It was a funky deal.
The only thing real was red,
Red blood around his red, red beard.

It was a funky deal.

In the beginning was the word,
And in the end the deed.
Judas did it to Jesus
For the same Herd. Same reason.
You made them mad, Malcolm. Same reason.

It was a funky deal.

You rocked too many boats, man.
Pulled too many coats, man.
Saw through the jive.
You reached the wild guys
Like me. You and Bird. (And that
Lil LeRoi cat.)

It was a funky deal.

Etheridge Knight

Aardvark

Since

      Malcolm died

      That old aardvark

      has got a sort of fame

      for himself —

      I mean, of late, when I read

      The dictionary the first

      Thing I see

      Is that animal staring at me.

And then

      I think of Malcolm —

      How he read

      in the prisons

      And on the planes

      And everywhere

      And how he wrote

      About old Aardvark.

Looks like Malcolm X helped

Bring attention to a lot of things

We never thought about before.

Julia Fields

Malcolm

You opened my eyes,
offered me a chance to see,
I saw.

Then I closed my eyes,
and cried, because I did not
wish to see.

Now, I look with eyes that are
brighter, but I am sad, because
you who made me see have gone from sight.

Kattie M. Cumbo

i remember . . .

i remember . . .
january,
1968
it's snow,
the desire that i had to build
a black snowman
and place him upon
Malcolm's grave.

Mae Jackson

October 16: The Raid

Perhaps
You will remember
John Brown.

John Brown
Who took his gun,
Took twenty-one companions
White and black,
Went to shoot your way to freedom
Where two rivers meet
And the hills of the
South
Look slow at one another —
And died
For your sake.

Now that you are
Many years free,
And the echo of the Civil War
Has passed away,

And Brown himself
Has long been tried at law,
Hanged by the neck,
And buried in the ground —
Since Harpers Ferry
Is alive with ghosts today,
Immortal raiders
Come again to town —

Perhaps
You will recall
John Brown.

Langston Hughes

RIGHT ON:
WHITE
AMERICA

America

If an eagle be imprisoned
on the back of a coin,
and the coin be tossed
into the sky,
the coin will spin,
the coin will flutter,
but the eagle will never fly.

Henry Dumas

America

America
Is a fairyland fraud
Where democracy is pronounced,
Dippity-Do
Ten times on a T.V. commercial —
Insulting my
Black mother,
My black sister,
My black wife,
         My black self.

                    Bobb Hamilton

Watts

Must I shoot the
white man dead
to free the nigger
in his head?

                    Conrad Kent Rivers

right on: white america

this country might have
been a pio
            neer land
once.
    but.   there ain't
no mo
        indians   blowing
custer's mind
            with a different
image of america.
                    this country
might have
            needed shoot/
outs/ daily/
        once.
                    but. there ain't
no mo real/ white/   allamerican
                            bad/guys.
just.
    u & me.
            blk/ and un/armed.
this country might have
been a pion
            eer land.   once.
                        and it still is.
check out
        the falling
gun/shells   on our blk/ tomorrows.

Sonia Sanchez

Children's Rhymes

By what sends
the white kids
I ain't sent:
I know I can't
be President.

What don't bug
them white kids
sure bugs me:
We know everybody
ain't free.

Lies written down
for white folks
ain't for us a-tall:
Liberty And Justice —
Huh! — For *All?*

Langston Hughes

Of Man and Nature

I like best
those things that
were here
before man started
building.

I like the open sky
that will not lie.
Not these city buildings
scraping the sky with
lies, and lies, and lies.

Horace Mungin

Feeding the Lions

They come into
our neighborhood
with the sun
an army of
social workers
carrying briefcases
filled with lies
and stupid grins
Passing out relief
checks
and food stamps
hustling from one
apartment to another
so they can fill
their quota
and get back out
before dark.

Norman Jordan

Dark People

Dark people line the sidewalks of the street after dark,
they dress the doorways with their bodies, crowd the
                                                    stoops,
dark people do.

Dark people sit around on boxes, garbage cans, 'cause
it's hot after dark. They sip soda, drink beer,
dark people do.

Dark people have no place to go, no money to go
                                        no-place with
and it's crowded and hot upstairs, like no air,
just stink from the halls, the alleyways, where
dark people throw their dirt and garbage after dark,
dark people do.

Dark people live on streets to the east and west, which
are the worse streets after dark. But dark people enjoy
their life the best they can in their dark world,
dark people do.

Kattie M. Cumbo

You Know, Joe

You know, Joe, it's a funny thing, Joe!
You worried most of your life about me,
Always afraid I'd get a job with you,
Always scared I might get served with you,
Always afraid I'd wanna love your sister,
or that she might love me.

Didn't want me to eat with you,
scared I might sit with you,
but with that Atom Bomb, Joe,
looks like I'm gonna die with you!

Don't seem right, does it, Joe?
Ought to have a separate bomb for colored!

Ray Durem

Vietnam #4

a cat said
on the corner

the other day
dig man

how come so many
of us
niggers

are dying over there
in that white
man's war

they say more of us
are dying

than them peckerwoods
& it just
   don't make sense

unless it's true
that the honkeys

are trying to kill us out
with the same stone

they killing them other cats
with

you know, he said
two birds with one stone

Clarence Major

Vive Noir!

i
am going to rise
en masse
from Inner City
                sick
                of newyork ghettos
            chicago tenements
        l a's slums
weary
        of exhausted lands
        sagging privies
        saying yessur yessah
        yesSIR
        in an assortment
        of geographical dialects i
have seen my last
broken down plantation
even from a
distance
                i
will load all my goods
in '50 Chevy pickups '53
Fords fly United and '66
caddys l
        have packed in
        the old man and the old lady and
        wiped the children's noses
            I'm tired
                of hand me downs
                shut me ups
                    pin me ins
                        keep me outs

                    messing me over have
                just had it
            baby
        from
    you . . .
i'm
gonna spread out
over America
                intrude
my proud blackness
all
        over the place
                    i have wrested wheat fields
                    from the forests

                    turned rivers
                    from their courses

                    leveled mountains
                    at a word
                    festooned the land with
                    bridges
                            gemlike
                        on filaments of steel
                            moved
                    glistening towers of Babel in place

                    sweated a whole
                    civilization
                        now
                                i'm
                    gonna breathe fire
                    through flaming nostrils BURN
                        a place for

                    me
          in the skyscrapers and the
          school rooms on the green
          lawns and the white
          beaches

                 i'm
      gonna wear the robes and
      sit on the benches
      make the rules and make
      the arrests say
      who can and who
      can't

                baby you don't stand
                a
                chance
    i'm
          gonna put black angels
          in all the books and a black
          Christchild in Mary's arms i'm
          gonna make black bunnies black
          fairies black santas black
          nursery rhymes and
                          black

          ice cream
                 i'm
    gonna make it a
          crime
              to be anything BUT   black
    gonna make white
    a twentyfourhour
    lifetime
    J.O.B.

                              Mari Evans

War

NO!!

Anywhere my father goes
I want to go

       shoot down Japanese

        eheheheheh BAM!

All the people getting killed
I don't want nobody to see me in my grave
I'd rather be in the Air Force
I'd be flying.

When they try to kill you
they throw these hand grenades at you,
sometimes when it be raining.

It was a war

      they dead

        it was real —
This man had all these things on his neck
He got shot in his neck

He didn't even die

He suppose to die.

William Alfred McLean, Jr.
Age 10

BUT
HERE
I AM

The New Integrationist

I

seek

integration

of

negroes

with

 black

people.

Don L. Lee

Taxes

Income taxes,

every year — due,

Sales taxes,

I pay these too.

Luxury taxes,

maybe — one or two,

Black taxes,

on everything I do.

Don L. Lee

I / wonder why

I
wonder why
some

people
leave the
front

porch
light still
on

in
the burning
bright

hotness
of summer
day

noontime.

Tom Poole

Knoxville, Tennessee

I always like summer
best
you can eat fresh corn
from daddy's garden
and okra
and greens
and cabbage
and lots of
barbecue
and buttermilk
and homemade ice–cream
at the church picnic
and listen to
gospel music
outside
at the church
homecoming
and go to the mountains with
your grandmother
and go barefooted
and be warm
all the time
not only when you go to bed
and sleep

Nikki Giovanni

Lineage

My grandmothers were strong.
They followed plows and bent to toil.
They moved through fields sowing seed.
They touched earth and grain grew.
They were full of sturdiness and singing.
My grandmothers were strong.

My grandmothers are full of memories
Smelling of soap and onions and wet clay
With veins rolling roughly over quick hands
They have many clean words to say.
My grandmothers were strong.
Why am I not as they?

Margaret Walker

Blues

Liquor don't drown,
    Smoke don't blow away
      The blues.

Money can't stall,
    Love can't scare away
      The blues.

Doors don't lock out,
    Shutters don't shut away
      The blues.

Nights stay lonely,
    Mornings always bring
      The blues.

Quandra Prettyman

Blues

Blues is a fine
sister
two feet tall.

Blues is a Monday
morning and
that ain't all.

Blues is nothing
when it's in your pocket
and your stomach.

Blues is a work
week that lasts
so long.
Blues is a paycheck
that's gotten, then gone.

Blues is a sweet song.
Some 'the time.
Blues is that
little black gal
of mine.

Horace Mungin

Get Up, Blues

Blues
Never climb a hill
Or sit on a roof
In starlight.

Blues
Just bend low
And moan in the street
And shake a borrowed cup.

Blues
Just sit around
Sipping,
Hatching yesterdays.

Get up, Blues.
Fly.
Learn what it means
To be up high.

James A. Emanuel

The Blues Today

rhythm and blues
ain't what it use to be
blues done gone and got
americanize
tellin' me that i should
stay in school
get off the streets
and keep the summer cool

i says
      blues ain't nothing like it use to be
blues done gone and got
americanize

blues done gone and lost its soul
and the folks singing it
ain't singing for me
no more

Mae Jackson

63

SOMETIMES ON MY WAY BACK DOWN TO THE BLOCK

I SEE THE SUN
AND IT LOOK FUNNY
REAL RED AND BIG
I PASS BIG BUILDINGS
AND NICE GRASS AND TREES
I LOOK EVERYWHERE
ON MY WAY BACK TO THE BLOCK
LOOK FOR PRETTY THINGS
I STOP AT A BIG LIBRARY
AND LOOK AT BIG BOOKS
BUT THEY DON'T SAY MUCH ON THE BLOCK
SOMETIMES I TAKE SUBWAY DOWN TO THE BLOCK
AND I SEE MOSTLY DARKNESS
THAT'S MORE LIKE MY BLOCK
I LIKE TO THINK AND FORGET
ON MY WAY DOWN TO THE BLOCK
AND CURSE AND WHISTLE
I LIKE TO HATE TOO
I LIKE TO BURN
I LIKE TO FIGHT
SOMETIMES ON MY WAY BACK TO THE BLOCK.

Victor Hernandez Cruz

MAN I THOUGHT YOU WAS TALKING
ANOTHER LANGUAGE THAT DAY

I WASN'T BORN HERE MAN
BUT HERE I AM
EVERYONE WAS FREEZING LAST NIGHT
I HAD THIS FUNNY FEEL IN MY STOMACH TODAY
TODAY THESE COPS COME DOWN THE BLOCK
AND THEY BEAT TITO ON THE HEAD
TOMORROW ·THEY DO THE SAME
STILL I WASN'T BORN HERE MAN
TONIGHT NOTHING TO DO
BUT MAYBE LISTEN TO FOOTSTEPS
MAYBE IT WILL RAIN AND I COULD LISTEN TO THAT
OR I COULD SING OR SOMETHING
I WASN'T BORN HERE MAN
BUT HERE I AM.

Victor Hernandez Cruz

YOU ARE LOVED, AWAKE OR DREAMING

from: Cities # 8

little cousins
play on your
fingers & head
& want kisses
before you leave.

Victor Hernandez Cruz

224 STOOP

I SAW BUTCH
HE WENT ON A HIGH CLOUD
TOLD ME HE WAS AFRO
TOLD ME HE WAS PROUD.

Victor Hernandez Cruz

Number 5 — December

Nobody knows me
when I go round
late at night
scratching on windows
& whispering in hallways
looking for someone
who loves me in the daytime
to take me in
at night

David Henderson

Frightened Flower

We walk back from the movies.
I close up like a frightened flower.

William J. Harris

69

On Wearing Ears

As long as people
continue to wear
ears
there won't
be much
peace and quiet
in this world.

William J. Harris

A Love Song

Do I love you?
I'll tell you true.

Do chickens have lips?
Do pythons have hips?

Do penguins have arms?
Do spiders have charms?

Do oysters get colds?
Do leopards have moles?

Does a bird cage make a zoo?
Do I love you?

Raymond Richard Patterson

71

i used to wrap my white doll up in

i used to wrap my white doll up in
an old towel
and place her upon my chest
i used to sing those funny old school songs
god bless america
my country 'tis of thee
when i was young
and very colored

Mae Jackson

Childhood

When I was a child I knew red miners
dressed raggedly and wearing carbide lamps.
I saw them come down red hills to their camps
dyed with red dust from old Ishkooda mines.
Night after night I met them on the roads,
or on the streets in town I caught their glance;
the swing of dinner buckets in their hands,
and grumbling undermining all their words.

I also lived in low cotton country
where moonlight hovered over ripe haystacks,
or stumps of trees, and croppers' rotting shacks
with famine, terror, flood, and plague near by;
where sentiment and hatred still held sway
and only bitter land was washed away.

Margaret Walker

from: Glimpses # xii

The old man walks to me;
    A piece of candy . . .
"Thank you sir!"
What do you say?
"Thank you sir . . . nice!"
Let's walk through the park
Feed the pigeons   smell the air . . .

A band is there this afternoon
Bring your pup along!
We'll get more sweets and make a day of it!
We will not litter the grass
    Till I am under it —
But that is not today . . .

Lawrence McGaugh

Crawl into bed

Crawl into bed.
Cover your head.
Stay very quiet.
Pretend very dead.

Quandra Prettyman

74

lullaby

sleep, love, sleep,
just such peace
as you seem
to lie in
there to dream
is my least
gift, love, sleep.

sleep, love, sleep,
while I watch
here close by,
no harm comes,
rest easy,
good dreams catch
you, love, sleep.

sleep, love, sleep,
no thing brings
me greater
comfort than
being here
while your thoughts
sleep, love, sleep.

Quandra Prettyman

Response

for Eileen

Sleep, little one, sleep for me,
Sleep the deep sleep of love.
You are loved, awake or dreaming,
You are loved.

Dancing winds will sing for you,
Ancient gods will pray for you,
A poor lost poet will love you,
As stars appear
In the dark
Skies.

Bob Kaufman

BIOGRAPHICAL NOTES

IMAMU AMEER BARAKA (LEROI JONES) was born in Newark, New Jersey, in 1934. He is the author of plays, a novel, short stories, essays and poems. *The Dead Lecturer* (1964) is a collection of his poetry. In 1968 he edited (together with Larry Neal) *Black Fire: An Anthology of Afro-American Writing.* He is the director of Spirit House, a community organization in Newark.

GWENDOLYN BROOKS was born in Topeka, Kansas, but has spent most of her life in Chicago, Illinois. In 1950 she won a Pulitzer prize for her second book of poems, *Annie Allen. In the Mecca,* a collection of poems dealing with Chicago's Black community, was published in 1968.

CHARLES COOPER's birthplace is Oakland, California. The year, 1948. He is a drama major at California State College and is also interested in music and art. Some of his poetry appeared in the anthology *Nine Black Poets* (1968).

VICTOR HERNANDEZ CRUZ was born in Puerto Rico in 1949 and came to New York City at the age of four. He grew up in *El Barrio,* or Spanish Harlem, in New York City, and he now lives and works in Berkeley, California. *Snaps,* his first collection of poetry, was published in 1968.

KATTIE M. CUMBO is a student at Long Island University. She hopes to make journalism her career and often contributes articles to American and African magazines. Her weekly column, "A Song from Brooklyn," appears in the *Morning Post* of Lagos, Nigeria.

DJANGATOLUM (LLOYD M. CORBIN, JR.) was born in Harlem, in New York City. He joined Clarence Major's summer writer's workshop in New York in 1967, when he was only seventeen. Since then he has continued to study and write, and his poems have appeared in student magazines and in poetry collections. He now attends Brandeis University in Massachusetts.

HENRY DUMAS was born in Arkansas and came to Harlem when he was ten years old. He attended Rutgers University in New Jersey and later taught at Hiram College in Ohio. His poetry and prose have appeared in many magazines. He had completed his first novel when he was shot and killed by a white policeman on the Harlem station platform of the New York Central Railroad in 1968.

RAY DUREM was born in Seattle, Washington, in 1915, and died of cancer in 1963. He was a veteran of the Spanish Civil War and, for many years, made his home in Mexico. His poems have appeared in numerous magazines and anthologies, and a volume of his poetry is being prepared for publication.

JAMES A. EMANUEL, a native Nebraskan, was born in 1921 and received a Ph.D. from Columbia University in New York in 1962. He teaches English at the City University of New York and is the author of many essays on Black American writing. His special interest in the work of Langston Hughes is reflected in his book of that title published in 1967.

MARI EVANS, a native of Toledo, Ohio, is Writer-in-Residence at Indiana University-Purdue University, Indianapolis, and also producer-director of a weekly half-hour TV series, "The Black Experience." Formerly an industrial editor, she was a John Hay Whitney Fellow, 1965-66. Her poetry has appeared widely in American and European anthologies and in textbooks.

JULIA FIELDS' birthplace is Uniontown, Alabama, and she was graduated from Knoxville College in Tennessee. A collection of her verse, *Poems,* was published in 1968. She lives with her husband and two children in Scotland Neck, North Carolina.

NIKKI GIOVANNI's birthplace is Knoxville, Tennessee. She attended Fisk University and the University of Pennsylvania. *Black Judgement,* a collection of her poems, appeared in 1968. She also writes short stories and essays, and is an editor of *Black Dialogue* magazine.

BOBB HAMILTON is a poet and short story writer who lives in New York City. He is an editor of *Soulbook,* a magazine, and is an instructor in Black literature and history at Queens College in New York.

WILLIAM J. HARRIS was born in Yellow Springs, Ohio. He was graduated from Central State College in nearby Wilberforce and is now a graduate student and instructor at Stanford University. His poems are included in the anthology *Nine Black Poets* (1968).

DAVID HENDERSON was born and educated in New York City. He is a teacher at the City University of New York. *Felix of the Silent Forest,* a collection of his poems, was published in 1967.

CALVIN C. HERNTON was born in Chattanooga, Tennessee, and was educated at Talladega College and Fisk University, both in Alabama. He is a sociologist and the author of *White Papers for White Americans* (1966).

LANGSTON HUGHES was born in Joplin, Missouri, in 1902 and died in New York City in 1967. During his forty-year career he wrote novels, short stories, plays, books for children, and many volumes of poetry. His books of poetry include *Selected Poems* (1959) and *The Panther and the Lash* (1967).

MAE JACKSON was born in Earl, Arkansas. She attended high school in Brooklyn, New York, where she has lived for the past ten years. She has been a song writer and a singer and is active in the Freedom Movement. A book of her collected poems, *Can I Poet with You?,* for which she has received the Conrad Kent Rivers Poetry Award, was published in 1969.

TED JOANS was born in Cairo, Illinois, in 1928, and is a painter and jazz musician as well as a writer. Although he has lived in Africa and Europe for many years, his work continues to be published in American magazines and anthologies. *Black Pow-Wow* was published in 1969.

ALICIA LOY JOHNSON, a native of Chicago, Illinois, is a student at Southern Illinois University in Carbondale. Her work has been published in many magazines, and in 1967 she won first prize in a poetry contest sponsored by Gwendolyn Brooks.

NORMAN JORDAN was born in Ansted, West Virginia, in 1938. He is a playwright as well as poet and works with the students of the Muntu Workshop in Cleveland, Ohio, where he makes his home.

BOB KAUFMAN gained fame as a poet in San Francisco during the 1950's, although for years his work was better known in Europe than in America. His books include *Solitudes Crowded with Loneliness* (1965) and *Golden Sardine* (1967).

ETHERIDGE KNIGHT was born in Corinth, Mississippi, in 1933. His book *Poems from Prison* was published in 1968, while he was still an inmate in Indiana State Prison. Mr. Knight has been released from prison and is continuing his writing career. He is married to poet Sonia Sanchez.

DON L. LEE's birthplace is Chicago, Illinois, and he is a staff member of The Museum of African-American History in that city. He has taught Afro-American literature and history at Columbia College and Roosevelt University, both in Chicago. His volumes of poetry include *Think Black!* (1967), *Black Pride* (1968) and *Don't Cry, Scream* (1969).

CLARENCE MAJOR was born in Atlanta, Georgia. He writes novels and articles as well as poetry, and his work has appeared in many magazines. He is the editor of *The New Black Poetry* (1969), an anthology devoted to the writing of young poets.

WILLIAM ALFRED MacLEAN, JR., was ten years old in 1969 when his poem, "War," was published. He attends school in New York City and, with a group of young writers, works on a magazine, *First Issue*.

LAWRENCE McGAUGH was born in Newton, Kansas, in 1940. He studied painting at the San Francisco Art Institute and now makes his home in Berkeley, California. *A Fifth Sunday* (1965) was his first published volume of poetry. His *Vacuum Cantos and Other Poems* was published in 1969.

HORACE MUNGIN is a young poet who lives and writes in New York City. His books of poetry include: *Dope Hustler Jazz* (1968) and *Now See Here, Homes* (1969).

RAYMOND RICHARD PATTERSON is a native of New York who teaches in that city. He gives poetry readings throughout the state, and his poems have appeared in many magazines and anthologies.

A collection of his poems, *26 Ways of Looking at a Black Man,* was published in 1969.

TOM POOLE was born in Asheville, North Carolina, in 1938. He is a research analyst and lives in New York City. His work has appeared in *The New Black Poetry* (1969), an anthology edited by Clarence Major.

QUANDRA PRETTYMAN, whose birthplace is Baltimore, Maryland, attended Antioch College in Ohio and the University of Michigan. She makes her home in New York City, where she has been a college teacher and book editor.

DUDLEY RANDALL was born in Washington, D.C., in 1914 and was graduated from Wayne State University in Michigan in 1945. He received an M.A. in library science from the University of Michigan. He has been a librarian in Detroit, where he makes his home, and is the publisher of Broadside Press in that city.

CONRAD KENT RIVERS was born in Atlantic City, New Jersey, in 1933 and died suddenly in March, 1968. He lived in Chicago, Illinois, and taught high school in Gary, Indiana. *The Still Voice of Harlem,* a collection of his poems, was published in 1968.

SONIA SANCHEZ was born in Birmingham, Alabama. She was educated at New York University and Hunter College, both in New York City, and has taught at San Francisco State College. Her poetry has been published in many magazines. She is married to Etheridge Knight.

LARRY THOMPSON was born in Seneca, South Carolina, in 1950, and was raised and educated in Harlem. He is a student at Yale University and an editor of the Yale literary magazine. His poetry has been published in *Negro Digest.*

MARGARET WALKER was born in Birmingham, Alabama. She was educated at the University of Iowa, and has taught and lectured at many colleges. *For My People,* her first book of poetry, won the Yale Series of Younger Poets Award in 1942. Her prize-winning novel, *Jubilee,* was published in 1966.

INDEX TO AUTHORS

INDEX TO TITLES

INDEX TO FIRST LINES

ACKNOWLEDGMENTS   cont.

Broadside Press for "Martin Luther King Jr." by Gwendolyn Brooks; "My Ace of Spades" by Ted Joans from *For Malcolm* (1967) edited by Dudley Randall and Margaret G. Burroughs; "It Was a Funky Deal" from *Poems from Prison* (1968) by Etheridge Knight; and "Awareness," "The New Integrationist" and "Taxes" from *Think Black!* (1967) by Don. L. Lee.

Brother's Distributing Co. for "Of Man and Nature" from *Dope Hustler Jazz* (1968) by Horace Mungin; and "Blues" from *Now See Here, Homes* (1969) by Horace Mungin.

Victor Hernandez Cruz for his "SOMETIMES ON MY WAY BACK DOWN TO THE BLOCK," "MAN I THOUGHT YOU WAS TALKING ANOTHER LANGUAGE THAT DAY" (and use of one line as section title) and "224 STOOP." All first appeared in *Evergreen*.

Djangatolum (Lloyd M. Corbin, Jr.) for his "Ali." First appeared in *CAW!*

Loretta Dumas and Eugene Redmond for "Image," by Henry Dumas, first appeared in *Umbra*; and "America" by Henry Dumas, first appeared in *Negro Digest*.

Dorothy Durem for "You Know, Joe" by Ray Durem.

James A. Emanuel for his "Get Up, Blues."

Mari Evans for her "The Alarm Clock," "Langston," and "Vive Noir!" All first appeared in *Negro Digest*.

Nikki Giovanni for "Word Poem (Perhaps Worth Considering)" and "Poem (No Name No. 2)" from her *Black Feeling, Black Talk;* and "My Poem," "The Funeral of Martin Luther King, Jr." and "Knoxville, Tennessee" from her *Black Judgement*.

Bobb Hamilton for his "America." First appeared in *Negro Digest*.

David Henderson for "Number 5—December" from *Felix of the Silent Forest*, The Poets' Press, San Francisco, Copyright 1967 by David Henderson.

Hill & Wang, Inc., for "The Truth" from *Black Pow-Wow* by Ted Joans, Copyright © 1969 by Ted Joans. Reprinted by permission of the Publisher.

Indiana University Press for "The Distant Drum" (and use of one line as section ii title) by Calvin C. Hernton from *The New Negro Poets: U.S.A.* edited by Langston Hughes, Copyright © 1964 by Langston Hughes.

International Publishers Co., Inc., for "Feeding the Lions" by Norman Jordan; "I" by Tom Poole; and "Blackberry Sweet" by Dudley Randall. All from *The New Black Poetry* by Clarence Major.

Alfred A. Knopf, Inc., for "Color" and "October 16: The Raid" (and use of one line as section iii title) by Langston Hughes, Copyright © 1967 by Arna Bontemps and George Houston Bass; and "Children's Rhymes," Copyright 1951 by Langston Hughes. All from *The Panther and the Lash* by Langston Hughes. Reprinted by permission of the Publisher.

Don L. Lee for his "Assassination."

Sterling Lord Agency for "We Own the Night" by Imamu Ameer Baraka (LeRoi Jones) from *Black Fire* edited by LeRoi Jones and Larry Neal, Copyright © 1968 by LeRoi Jones and Larry Neal. Reprinted by permission of the Agent.

William Alfred MacLean, Jr., for his "War."

Clarence Major for his "Vietnam #4" from *Where Is Vietnam* edited by Walter Lowenfels.

Lawrence McGaugh for "Glimpses #XII" from his *A Fifth Sunday*, Oyez, Berkeley, Copyright 1965 by Lawrence McGaugh.

Moore Publishing Co. for "Idle Chatter" by Charles Cooper; "Washiri (Poet)," "Malcolm" and "Dark People" by Kattie M. Cumbo; "Aardvark" by Julia Fields; "The Truth Is Quite Messy," "An Historic Moment," "Frightened Flower" and "On Wearing Ears" by William J. Harris; and "A Black Poetry Day" by Alicia Loy Johnson.

New Directions Publishing Corp. for "Response" (and use of one line as section vi title) from *Solitudes Crowded with Loneliness* by Bob Kaufman, Copyright © 1965 by Bob Kaufman. Reprinted by permission of the Publisher.

Raymond Richard Patterson for "Black All Day" (and use of title as section i title) from his *26 Ways of Looking at a Black Man and Other Poems,* Award Books, New York, Copyright © 1969 by Raymond Richard Patterson; and his "A Love Song," which is here published for the first time, Copyright © 1970 by Raymond Richard Patterson.

Quandra Prettyman for her "The Birth of the Poet," "Blues," "Crawl into Bed" and "Lullaby." All are here published for the first time, Copyright © 1970 by Quandra Prettyman Stadler.

Random House, Inc., for "Cities #8" from *SNAPS* by Victor Hernandez Cruz, Copyright © 1969 by Victor Hernandez Cruz. Reprinted by permission of the Publisher.

Sonia Sanchez for her "right on: white america" (and use of title as section iv title). First appeared in *Negro Digest*.

Larry Thompson for his "Black Is Best." First appeared in *Negro Digest*.

Yale University Press for "Lineage" and "Childhood" from *For My People* by Margaret Walker, Copyright © 1942 by Yale University Press.

The editor wishes to thank Hoyt Fuller of *Negro Digest*, Dudley Randall of Broadside Press, Nikki Giovanni of Black Dialogue Publications, John Stadler and Walter Lowenfels for their cooperation and their commitment to fine Black literature.

E. S. E. A. — TITLE II

Sacramento City Unified School District